Contents

Your child and numeracy

From September 1999, after a trial year in 1998, most primary schools must carry out a daily numeracy session, to meet new standards set by the government.

What is numeracy?

Numeracy is defined by the national Numeracy Task Force in the following way:

"Numeracy means knowing about numbers and number operations. More than this, it requires an ability and inclination to solve numerical problems, including those involving money or measures. It also demands familiarity with the ways in which numerical information is gathered by counting and measuring, and is presented in graphs, charts and tables."

Numeracy in the primary school

Numerate primary pupils are expected to:
• understand the size of a number and its position in the number system;
• know number facts by heart – times tables, bonds, doubles, halves;
• use these facts to work out answers mentally;
• calculate accurately in mental and written work, using a range of methods;
• know when they should or should not use a calculator;
• check and correct their own answers;
• explain their methods using mathematical vocabulary;
• measure and estimate sensibly;
• analyse data in tables, charts and graphs.

Numeracy teaching

The daily numeracy session will include whole-class, group and independent work and will incorporate as much mental and oral calculation as possible. Your child's teacher will be happy to explain the school's policy to you.

Turn to page 40 for ways to help your child's numeracy skills.

How to use this book

As children progress through the Key Stage 1 years (ages 4–7), they acquire many reading, writing and mathematics skills which prepare for further education at Key Stage 2 and beyond.

Each book in this series is organised into 18 activity pages which provide practice in the skills your child will be developing at school.

Activities: Your child should use a pencil to fill in the activity pages. Take time to read any instructions together and to discuss the pictures.

Character: Gives tips, advice and key words.

Focus: The learning purpose of the page.

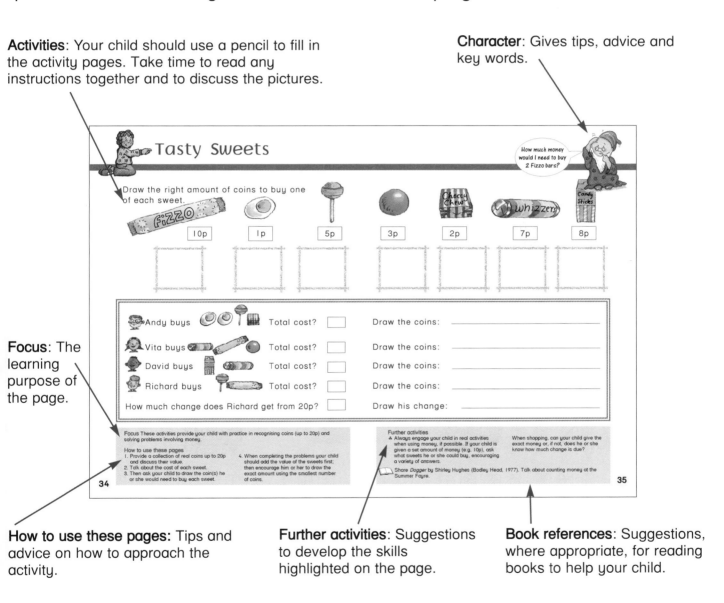

How to use these pages: Tips and advice on how to approach the activity.

Further activities: Suggestions to develop the skills highlighted on the page.

Book references: Suggestions, where appropriate, for reading books to help your child.

Remember, learning should be enjoyable. Work at your child's pace and emphasise successes rather than failures.

And finally, have fun!

Numbers Everywhere

Draw or cut out pictures of numbers and stick them here.

numbers everywhere

M284 SMJ

today!

Write the word or number.

one	1
	2
three	
	4
five	
	6
seven	
	8
nine	
	10

Write the numbers in the shapes.

eleven   twelve   thirteen   fourteen   fifteen

sixteen   seventeen   eighteen   nineteen   twenty

Focus These activities will help to increase your child's awareness of numbers in the environment, and provide practice in matching numerals and words up to 20.

How to use these pages
1. Ask your child to fill the box with examples of numbers in the environment.
2. Turn this activity into a game by setting a target of, say, finding 15 different places where numbers can be found.
3. Practise writing words for numbers.
4. Discuss with your child what would happen if there were no numbers on, for example, telephones, buses, etc.
5. Fill in the missing numbers on page 5.

Fill in the missing numbers.

Further activities
- Ensure that your child can count up to at least 20 with no errors or omissions. Challenge him or her to count backwards.
- Continue with the collection of numbers, looking around you whenever you go out together.
- Playing board games such as 'Snakes and Ladders' helps practise sequencing numbers.
- Encourage your child to make up sets of numbers up to 20 in practical ways, e.g. sweets, buttons, etc.
- Extend the activity above by asking your child to show you ways to make 5, 10, 20 – e.g. 2 + 3 makes 5, and 1 + 4 makes 5.

Skiing Sums

Fill in the correct answers.

How many people are wearing red hats? ☐

How many are wearing blue hats? ☐

How many are wearing hats altogether? ☐

0   1   2   3   4   5   6   7   8   9   10

Focus These activities provide practice for your child in completing addition operations using quick recall of facts to 20.

How to use these pages

1. Ask your child to complete the two-number sums, encouraging mental strategies and counting on as well as using the number line and/or apparatus.

2. Ask him or her to count the objects and fill in the answers.

How many are in blue coats?	☐
How many are in yellow coats?	☐
How many are in orange coats?	☐
How many people altogether?	☐

| 11 | 12 | 13 | 14 | 15 | 16 | 17 | 18 | 19 | 20 |

Further activities

▶ Encourage your child to respond rapidly to quick-fire oral questions in context, e.g. 'What is 11p add 7p?', 'Give me two numbers that add up to 18', 'If one pear costs 8p, what do two pears cost?'

 Share *Each Peach Pear Plum* by Janet and Allan Ahlberg (Puffin Books, 1989). Count the objects as the story progresses.

Magic Munching

This magnificent Magic Munching Machine makes numbers smaller.
It takes away 4 from every number that is put in.

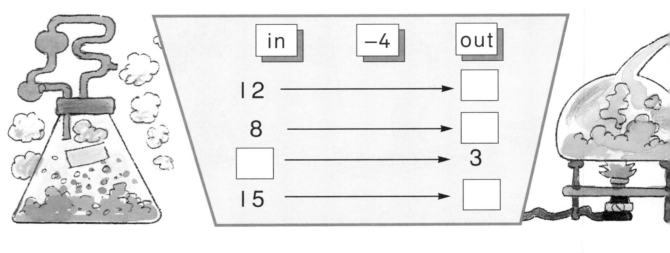

in	−4	out
12	→	☐
8	→	☐
☐	→	3
15	→	☐

What do these machines do?

in 12   out 9

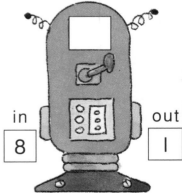

in 8   out 1

Focus These activities will help your child to understand the operation of subtraction as 'taking away', and to find the difference between two numbers.

How to use these pages

1. Work through the activities systematically. It may be necessary for your child to use counters so he or she can see the physical reduction when an amount is taken away from a different number. You might like to use the number line on the previous page, too.

2. It is important to encourage your child to talk about what the machine is doing as he or she works out the answers.

Machines

'Take away' is also known as 'subtract' and 'minus'.

What number comes out?

out

$- 4$

$8 - 4 = \boxed{}$

$\boxed{} - 6 = 2$

$5 - \boxed{} = 1$

$9 - 6 = \boxed{}$

$14 - 4 = \boxed{}$

$7 - \boxed{} = 4$

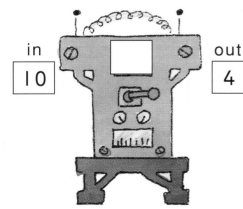

in
$\boxed{10}$

out
$\boxed{4}$

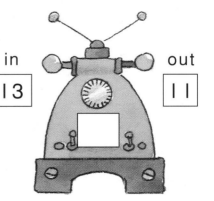

in
$\boxed{13}$

out
$\boxed{11}$

Further activities

▶ Make a function machine together from an empty cereal or shoe box. Make cards to go in it, with your child writing out the answer card depending on the machine's function. Your machine can add as well as subtract.

▶ Use different vocabulary when doing oral subtraction in context, e.g. 'What is the difference…?', 'How many are left?', and use the terms 'take away', 'subtract', 'minus', so your child can approach a variety of problems confidently.

Shape Fun

Draw a line from the shaded face to the right shape.
Then write the names of the flat shapes.

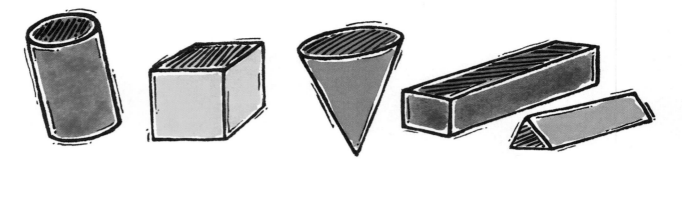

c_____   r_____   t_____   s_____   o_____

Finish these patterns.

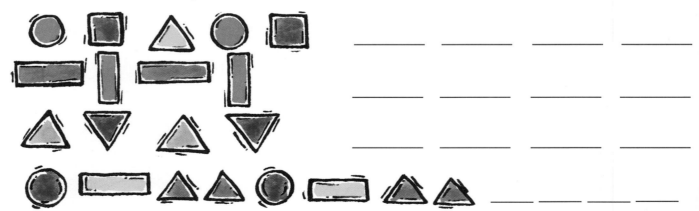

_____ _____ _____ _____

_____ _____ _____ _____

_____ _____ _____ _____

_____ _____ _____ _____

Can you make a wizard from solid shapes?

Collect some boxes and shapes to make junk models.

Make a castle out of boxes. Draw it here.

Write the number of shapes you used.

cylinders ☐

cuboids ☐

cubes ☐

cones ☐

spheres ☐

other shapes ☐

Draw a line from the firework to its correct shape.

| cuboid | pyramid | sphere | cube | cylinder |

Further activities
- ▶ Use modelling clay and drinking straws, or commercially produced construction kits, to build 3-D shapes.
- ▶ Ask your child to sort and classify the 3-D shapes he or she has made and collected using different criteria.

- ▶ Encourage your child to draw 3-D shapes from different views in order to visualise the whole shape.
- ▶ Use 3-D shapes for printing, encouraging your child to recognise the 2-D faces.

Noah's Ark

The animals went in one by one,
the elephant chewing a sticky bun.

The animals went in two by two,
the rhinoceros and the kangaroo.

The animals went in three by three,
the wasp, the flea and the bumble bee.

The animals went in four by four,
the great hippopotamus stuck in the door.

The animals went in five by five,
with great big trunks they did arrive.

The animals went in six by six,
the hyena laughed at the monkey's tricks.

How many fleas can you see? ☐
How many birds were there? ☐
How many ants can you see? ☐
How many animals can you see altogether? ☐

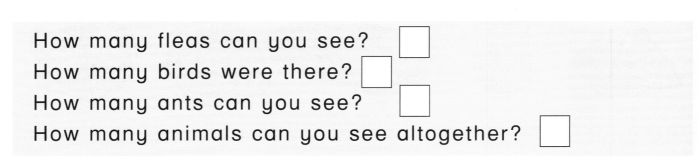

Focus These activities provide your child with an opportunity to sequence numbers and count using a number rhyme.

How to use these pages
1. Talk about the story of 'Noah's Ark' with your child (you might like to explain that this story forms part of one set of people's beliefs, if appropriate).

2. Then sing (or say) the song, encouraging your child to join in whenever he or she can.
3. Encourage your child to answer the questions, using the pictures.

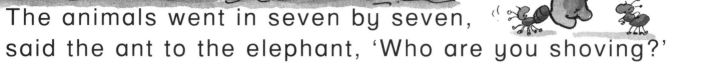

5 wasps add 6 bees.... how many insects altogether?

The animals went in seven by seven,
said the ant to the elephant, 'Who are you shoving?'

The animals went in eight by eight,
the worm was early, the birds were late.

The animals went in nine by nine,
some had water and some had wine.

The animals went in ten by ten,
if you want more you must sing it again.

And they all went into the Ark,
just to get out of the rain.

Can you think of animals that begin with the same letters as these numbers?

one   two   three   four   five   six   seven   eight   nine   ten

Here's one: one begins with the same letter as octopus.

Further activities

▶ Work with your child to create number tongue twisters, e.g. two terrible terrapins tickling tall trees. These are fun to illustrate, too!

▶ Write your own number poem, and illustrate it with your child.

 Share *Noah's Ark* by Lucy Cousins (Walker Books, 1993). Compare the poem above with the story, and count the animals in twos.

Crazy Shapes

You will need:
- scissors
- a piece of paper

What is the longest spiral you can make from the sheet of paper?
Try a round spiral and a square one.

You will need:
- shape templates
- coloured pencils

Draw a shape picture using the templates.

Try a seaside picture or a space picture.

How many different shapes did you use?

Focus These activities will increase your child's awareness of regular and irregular shapes through creative activities.

How to use these pages
1. Provide your child with the necessary equipment (take care using scissors!). Buy or make templates of squares, circles, triangles and rectangles.
2. Work through the activities, encouraging your child to talk about each shape as he or she handles it. These activities are open-ended and increase shape identification and properties while developing fine motor skills.

Have lots of fun making crazy shapes!

You will need:
• drinking straws
• modelling clay

Join the straws with modelling clay. How many different shapes can you make? ☐

You will need:
• a ruler
• a pencil
• coloured pencils
• a piece of paper

Colour your shapes	
3 sides	red
4 sides	yellow
5 sides	orange
6 sides	green

Use your ruler to draw a pattern on your paper.

Look at the shapes you have made.

Count the sides of each shape and write the numbers inside each shape.

Further activities

▶ Make a matching game using shapes. Draw equal numbers of pictures of regular shapes on cards. Write the names of the shape underneath each one. Then you and your child can play 'Snap', or 'Pelmanism' (put the cards facing down, then take turns to turn two over. If they match you keep the pair. If not, turn them face down again).

▶ Extend the game above by replacing half the cards with pictures of shapes cut from magazines. Then you and your child can match a picture of a clock with the card saying 'circle', for example.

Cool Cats

Fill in the chart.

	striped
lying down	_____ _____
	Tiddles _____
not lying down	_____

How many cats are there altogether?_____

How many cats are striped? _____

How many cats are lying down? _____

Where would a striped cat, lying down, go on the chart?

not striped

_____

_____

_____

_____

_____

_____

How many are striped and not lying down?_____
How many are not striped and not lying down?_____
How many are not striped and lying down? _____

Further activities
▶ Collect pictures of cats from stories or magazines. Where would each one fit in the Carroll diagram?

▶ Using a pack of playing cards, ask your child to sort them into four sets, i.e. picture cards and number cards, red cards and black cards. Encourage your child to discuss what he or she has done and question him or her while interpreting the data collected.

Tens and Ones

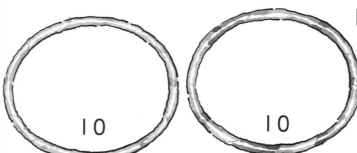

Count out 23 pencils.
Put them in piles of 10.
Draw them here.

How many are left over? ☐

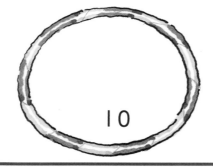

(10)   (10)

23 = ☐ tens and ☐ ones

Count out 13 socks
Put them in piles of 10.
Draw them here.

How many are left over? ☐

(10)

13 = ☐ tens and ☐ ones

Try these:

17 = ☐ tens and ☐ ones   35 = ☐ tens and ☐ ones
42 = ☐ tens and ☐ ones   27 = ☐ tens and ☐ ones

Focus These activities give your child practice in grouping quantities in tens and ones, which will help his or her counting skills.

How to use these pages
1. Start by finding out if your child can count in tens and write a sequence from 0 to 100.
2. Look at the numbers your child has written down. Does he or she notice anything about the numbers?
3. Use real objects for grouping in tens as you work through the problems together. Does your child see the value of each digit in a 2-digit number?

18

Can you count to 100 in tens?

How many cakes are there altogether?

2 tens + 5 ones = ☐ + ☐ = ☐

How many felt tips are there altogether?

10 felt tip pens   10 felt tip pens   10 felt tip pens

3 tens + 2 ones = ☐ + ☐ = ☐

Match the labels to the lottery balls with lines.

I ten + 8 ones	4 tens + 9 ones	0 tens + 9 ones
3 tens + 2 ones	4 tens + 8 ones	3 tens + 3 ones
2 tens + I one	2 tens + 3 ones	

32 23 48
49 18
9
33 21

Further activities

▶ Together, use 10p pieces and 1p pieces to exchange amounts of money, e.g. 83p is 8 x 10p coins and 3 x 1p coin, i.e. 8 tens + 3 ones.

▶ Compare two numbers, say 24 and 42. Ask your child which is more – how does he or she know?

19

All Year Round

Fill in the missing months on the calendar wheel.

November	October
July	February
April	June

Colour in the wheel.

Winter months	blue
Spring months	green
Summer months	yellow
Autumn months	red

Start here

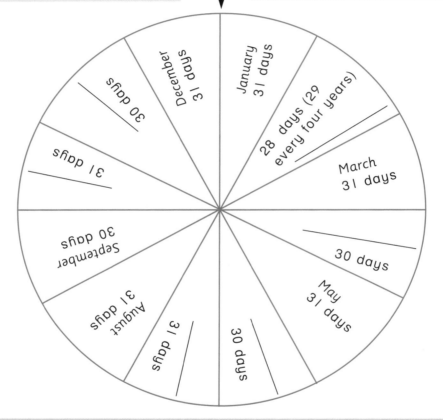

How many months are there in one year? _____

Which month comes between July and September? _____

How many days are there in January? _____

Focus These activities will encourage your child to understand and use the names of the months and seasons.

How to use these pages
1. Ask your child if he or she can remember the names of any months of the year. Write them all down and try to order them correctly.
2. Introduce the seasons – talk about the weather and its effects.
3. Complete the calendar wheel and use it to answer the questions.
4. Encourage your child to learn the rhyme and complete the activity. The first picture refers to your child's birthday month.

Can you say the months of the year in the right order?

Learn this rhyme.

30 days has September,
April, June and November.
All the rest have 31,
Except February, which has 28 clear,
And 29 in each Leap Year.

Write the months underneath the pictures.

Draw pictures for these months.

April

September

Made to Measure

How many hand spans will it take to measure these objects? Guess first, then measure!  hand span

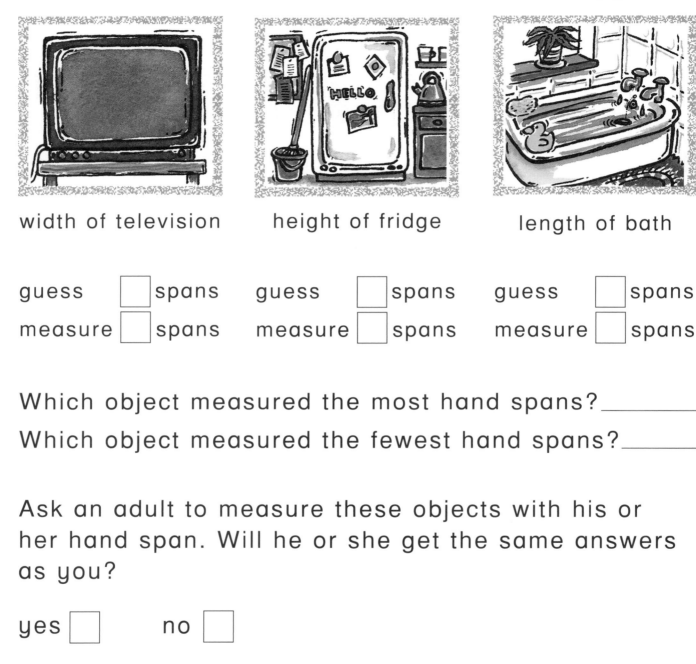

width of television   height of fridge   length of bath

guess ☐ spans   guess ☐ spans   guess ☐ spans

measure ☐ spans   measure ☐ spans   measure ☐ spans

Which object measured the most hand spans?_____

Which object measured the fewest hand spans?_____

Ask an adult to measure these objects with his or her hand span. Will he or she get the same answers as you?

yes ☐   no ☐

How wide is your bed in hand spans? Guess first!

Draw a circle around:

the longest recorder

the smallest drum

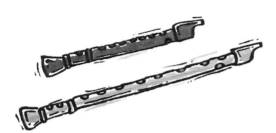

the widest maraca

the shortest guiro

the largest beater

Draw:

a long trumpet

a large guitar

a thin triangle

Further activities

► Your child could measure objects using other non-standard body measures, e.g. stride, cubit (elbow to finger tip), digit (width of finger). Always encourage estimation (guessing) first.

► Ordering objects, such as musical instruments, books, pencils according to size involves direct comparison in measure.

 Share *Billy's Sunflower* by Nicola Moon (Little Hippo, 1997). Discuss the height of the sunflower. You might like to grow your own and measure it as it grows.

Symmetry Shop

Half of everything is missing in the Symmetry Shop.
Can you complete the picture?

Focus These activities offer your child practice in completing symmetrical pictures and patterns.

How to use these pages

1. Together, look around your home to find objects which are symmetrical, i.e. they have a mirror line where both halves are the same.

2. As your child tackles the activity, encourage him or her to use a small mirror to show what the missing side looks like before completing the pattern or picture.

24

Can you draw the other half of me?

Further activities

▶ Cut out symmetrical pictures of faces, trees etc, and cut them in half. Stick one half onto paper and ask your child to complete the other side symmetrically.

▶ When you are out and about, encourage your child to identify symmetrical patterns in nature and the environment.

A Day Out

Write in the correct times.

1 | :00 | 7 o'clock

2 | 8:00 | ___ o'clock

4 | :00 | 10 o'clock

5 | 11:00 | ___ o'clock

7 | :00 | 3 o'clock

8 | :00 | 5 o'clock

Focus These activities provide your child with practice in matching analogue (clock face) times to digital displays and times in words.

How to use these pages

1. Before you start, make a paper clock face and attach paper hands using a paper fastener.
2. Talk with your child through the events of the day in chronological order, matching the hands of the clock to the time in words or digital display.
3. Help your child to fill in the missing numbers.

If I start my nap at 3 o'clock and wake up again at quarter past 3, how many minutes have I slept for?

3

:00

9 o'clock

6

1:00

___ o'clock

9

6:00

___ o'clock

Further activities

► Talk to your child about his or her typical day. Can he or she tell you at what time they do certain things in their usual routine?

► Try to make your child aware of time as much as possible. Match the time on clock faces and digital displays to regular events, e.g. the time school starts and ends.

► Encourage an awareness of days, weeks and months in everyday contexts wherever possible.

All About You

Write down these facts about yourself.

TOP SECRET

Name: _____

Age: _____

Date of birth: ☐ ☐ ☐

day   month year

Address: _____

_____

_____

Telephone number: _____

Shoe size: _____

Height: _____ cm

Weight: _____ kg

Number of brothers and sisters: _____

Favourite number: _____

Focus These activities provide your child with an opportunity to improve number handling.

How to use these pages
1. Talk through all the details required with your child. Encourage him or her to learn their date of birth, address and phone number.

2. Point out and talk about how, for example a telephone number is made from several numerals.
3. Ask your child to fill in their details and to complete the related problems.

I was born on 2/12/90. What's my magic number?

1. Add up the numerals in your date of birth (e.g. 09/07/91 is 0+9+0+7+9+1 = 26).

_____

This is your magic number.

2. Add your age and your shoe size.

_____

3. Add up the numbers in your telephone number (e.g. 894626 = 8+9+4+6+2+6 = 35).

_____

4. Can you take your age away from your favourite number?

_____

5. Which number is greater? Tick the right box ☑

your height in cm ☐   your shoe size ☐

your weight in kg ☐   your age ☐

6. Which is smaller? Tick the right box. ☑

your magic number ☐

your age and shoe number ☐

your favourite number ☐

your birthday month number ☐

Further activities

▶ Repeat the activity, this time using your details instead of your child's. Compare and discuss the two sets of details.

▶ Ask your child to make a collection of magic numbers for friends and family.

▶ Encourage mental addition of numbers to 20, by asking your child to add numbers in context, e.g. shopping, cooking.

At the Supermarket

This pictogram shows what was bought from the supermarket bakery.

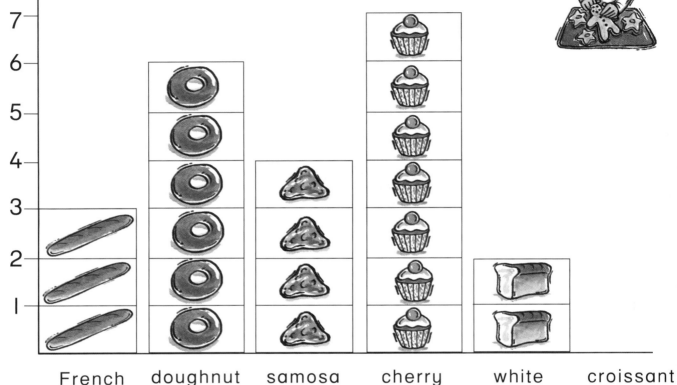

Five croissants 🥐 were sold. Show this on the chart.

Which was the most popular item? _____

How many doughnuts were bought? _____

How many more French sticks were
bought than white loaves? _____

How many items were bought altogether? _____

Put the supermarket objects in the diagram.

loaf of bread

baked beans

orange

toilet paper

eggs

chocolate bar

tin of polish

tomato ketchup

bin liners

box of cereal

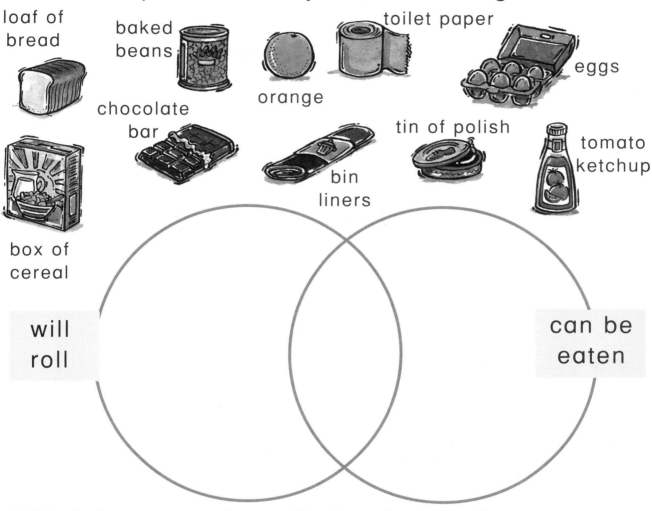

will roll

can be eaten

Which items can be rolled and eaten?

_____

Which items cannot be eaten?

_____

Further activities

▶ Encourage your child to cut out pictures of groups of foods from magazines and to represent them in a pictogram.

▶ Using real objects will help to consolidate your child's understanding of collecting, representing and interpreting data.

Cut out large circles of brown paper or newspaper and then use these as a Venn diagram in which to sort toys, clothing, etc. Sort the same objects according to different criteria.

33

Tasty Sweets

Draw the right amount of coins to buy one of each sweet.

10p	1p	5p

Andy buys 🥚🥚🍭🍬   Total cost? ▢

Vita buys 🍬🍬🫧   Total cost? ▢

David buys 🍬🍬   Total cost? ▢

Richard buys 🍭🍬   Total cost? ▢

How much change does Richard get from 20p? ▢

Focus These activities provide your child with practice in recognising coins (up to 20p) and solving problems involving money.

How to use these pages
1. Provide a collection of real coins up to 20p and discuss their value.
2. Talk about the cost of each sweet.
3. Then ask your child to draw the coin(s) he or she would need to buy each sweet.
4. When completing the problems your child should add the value of the sweets first; then encourage him or her to draw the exact amount using the smallest number of coins.

34

How much money would I need to buy 2 Fizzo bars?

Candy Sticks

| 3p | 2p | 7p | 8p |

Draw the coins: _____

Draw the coins: _____

Draw the coins: _____

Draw the coins: _____

Draw his change: _____

Further activities

▶ Always engage your child in real activities when using money, if possible. If your child is given a set amount of money (e.g. 10p), ask what sweets he or she could buy, encouraging a variety of answers.

When shopping, can your child give the exact money or, if not, does he or she know how much change is due?

 Share *Dogger* by Shirley Hughes (Bodley Head, 1977). Talk about counting money at the Summer Fayre.

35

Country Park

10

11 Dropped litter. Go back one space.

9

3

8 How many badgers? Move on 2 spaces.

2 How many deer? Move on 1 space.

7

4

1

5 Stop at viewpoint. Miss a turn.

6

Start

Focus These activities provide your child with an opportunity to use mathematics in a game: counting on, adding and subtracting.

How to use these pages

1. The game can be played by 2 to 4 players and each player will need a counter of some sort. You will also need a die.

2. Play the game with your child. Throw the die and move the correct number of spaces, following the instructions on the board. (You will need to check that your child has answered correctly.)

Play this game to practise your counting.

12 How many people walking? Move on that many spaces.

13

14

15 How many squirrels? Move on 1 space.

16

20 Lose your way. Go back 2 spaces.

19

18

17 Ranger's jeep broken down. Miss a turn.

21

26

27

22 How many rabbits? Move on that many spaces.

25 Help squirrel find nuts. Move on 1 space.

28 Stop for a picture. Miss a turn.

23

24

29

30

Finish

Further activities

▶ Discuss with your child what would happen if the die had only the numbers 1, 2 and 3 on it.

▶ If possible, visit a country park with your child and encourage him or her to make an 'I spy' number collection, e.g. spot 1 deer, 2 picnic benches, 3 squirrels, 4 oak trees, etc.

▶ Count objects in order as far as your child can manage. Try to extend his or her counting each time.

Children's Ward

Matthew

Grace

18 + 4 =

7 − 6 =

TOYS

Add the numbers at the end of each bed.

How many flowers can you see? ☐

What colour are the nurses' uniforms? _____

Who is lying next to Helen? _____

Who is lying to Grace's left? _____

How many nurses are there altogether? ☐

What colour are Grace's flowers? _____

Focus These activities bring together different elements of maths in a familiar scenario.

How to use these pages

1. Talk about the scene together, pointing out all the different objects, counting the objects, and asking your child what is happening.

2. Complete the questions, concentrating on one question at a time.

3. Encourage your child to invent some mathematical questions of his or her own about the scene.

What shape is the toy box? _____

How many more bottles are there on the top shelf than on the middle shelf? ▢

What time is it? _____

What colour are Matthew's pyjamas? _____

How long are visiting hours in the evening? _____

How many jugs are there? ▢

Further activities

▶ Every situation contains some mathematical element of counting, shape, colour, data handling, time, money etc. Look for and discuss as many as you can.

▶ Design and make a board game out of a trip to the dentist, waiting for a train etc. Together with your child try to include as many mathematical questions as possible.

Helping your child

Develop your child's mathematics skills

Learning about maths is not just about learning numbers. It is about developing an awareness of numbers in the environment, numbers in the street, at home, in the shops.

There are many ways to help your child develop his or her numeracy skills.

- Estimate and weigh fruit and vegetables in the supermarket. Guess quantities and perform mental calculations. Identify the coins that will be needed to buy items in the shop or work out the amount of change.

- Count the number of objects in the trolley and name the shapes of different packaging. Sort the packets according to different criteria.

- At home, lay the table, matching items in each setting and counting items. Encourage your child to help measure out ingredients, cut into halves and quarters and work out cooking times. Place different containers in order of capacity.

- Read analogue and digital clocks and relate the times to real events. Look again later and work out periods of time that have elapsed. Identify start and finish times of a television programme.

- Plant out bulbs and seeds in pots, counting as you do so. Use a calendar to work out when plants will flower.

- Look at different numbers used around the home, e.g. door numbers, telephone numbers and dates. Encourage your child to say the numbers aloud.

- Sort toys according to type, size, shape, etc. Set up a play shop, post office or restaurant using real money and objects. Construct shapes from modelling kits, Plasticine, junk. Encourage your child to use shape and positional language.

- Ask questions that require mental calculations such as: you have got 8 pencils, how many more do you need to have 12? Play board games using counters and dice.

- Ask how many circles can we count on our journey? Count objects and perform mental calculations.

- Compare sizes of objects, and match objects that are the same. Make collections of nature objects, such as leaves or twigs, and arrange in sets of similar weight.

Mix and Match Numbers 1-20

18	seven	
3	four	
6	nine	
9	two	
2	five	
5	eight	
7	one	
1	six	
4	ten	
10	three	

15	eighteen	
19	twenty	
16	fifteen	
12	sixteen	
20	thirteen	
13	nineteen	
17	eleven	
11	fourteen	
18	seventeen	
14	twelve	

The Super Subtraction Contraption

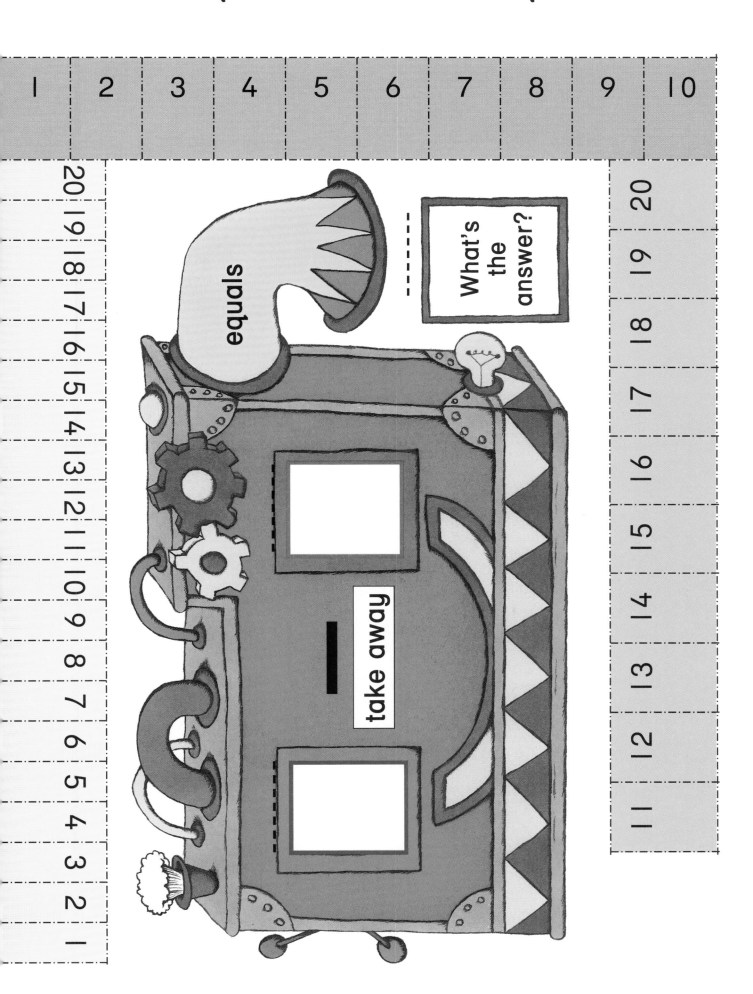

Our Class: Handling data

Amir	Jade	Katie
Rebecca	May	Rifa
Jason	Theo	Soraya

dark hair
fair hair
short hair
long hair
brown eyes
blue eyes
earrings
no earrings

➡

2

4

➡

1

3

⬆

⬆

Party Shapes: 3-D Shapes

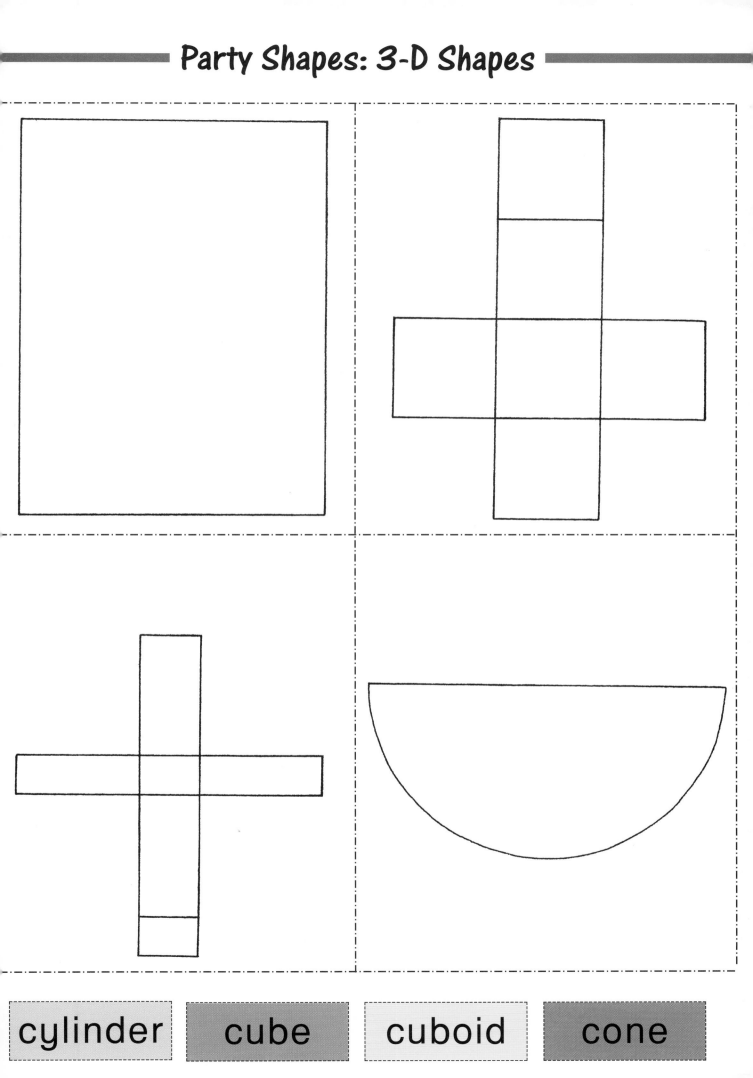

| cylinder | cube | cuboid | cone |